FOUR AND TWENTY BLACKBIRDS

FOUR & TWENTY BLACKBIRDS

NURSERY RHYMES *of* YESTERDAY
RECALLED FOR CHILDREN OF TO-DAY

COLLECTED *by* HELEN DEAN FISH

ILLUSTRATED *by* ROBERT LAWSON

J. B. LIPPINCOTT COMPANY
PHILADELPHIA NEW YORK

Eleventh Impression

Library of Congress catalog card number 37-22632

Printed in the United States of America

TO THE MEMORY
OF MY MOTHER

CONTENTS

6 JOE DOBSON

A traditional English nursery rhyme, found with many variants. This one, ascribed to "B.A.T." was published in London in 1807. "Printed for J. Harris, successor to E. Newbery, at the Original Juvenile Library, corner of St. Paul's Church Yard. Price One Shilling plain, & Eighteen-pence coloured." The earliest version of the tale appears in a 15th Century manuscript in the Chetham Library at Manchester, England.

Air on page 101.

7 POOR LADY DUMPLING

Found in an edition of Mother Goose's Melodies, published by Fisher and Brother, Philadelphia, before 1865.

8 OLD MOTHER TABBYSKINS

Anonymous. From "Our Children's Songs" Harper and Brothers, 1877. Also given in "National Nursery Rhymes" by J. W. Elliott, (London.)

Air on page 101.

9 THE HUNGRY FOX

Traditional, English. Found in many variants and often ascribed to Mother Goose. A song of the 15th Century, similar to it, is found in the *Reliquiæ Antiquæ*. This version is contributed by Mary Barling Street.

Air on page 102.

10 FROG WENT A-COURTING

Traditional, English, and found in many variants. This one has been handed down orally in the Southern Appalachian Mountains and is given as sung by the children at Pine Mountain School, Kentucky.

Air on page 102.

11 THE KEYS OF HEAVEN

A traditional English song found in many versions. The version given here is one passed down in many American homes from mother to child.

Air on page 102.

12 DAME TROT AND HER COMICAL CAT

Traditional, English. This version is from "Our Children's Songs," Harper and Brothers, 1877.

13 THE OLD CROW

Traditional, English, with variants. This version and tune is contributed by Laura E. Richards.

Air on page 103.

14 COME HITHER LITTLE PUPPY DOG

Of Mother Goose origin and found in early editions.

15 OLD CRUMMLES

Traditional, English. There are several variants. This version given as sung to Laura E. Richards by her mother.

Air on page 103.

16 JIM FINLEY'S PIG

Anonymous, and supplied for this collection by Mary M. Rogers, who recalls it as a treasure of her childhood.

17 WE ARE ALL NODDING

This appears in Lady Bell's "Singing Circle" as a traditional singing game, but is also remembered in many American homes as a lullaby. The first stanza, repeated at the end, is sure to send to sleep any child who may still be awake.

Air on page 104.

18 THE TRAGIC TALE OF HOOTY THE OWL

Traditional and probably of English origin. Contributed to this collection by Mary Barling Street.

19 THE TWO FOXES

Anonymous and dating probably about 1830, this poem is given as remembered by a *Boston Evening Transcript* contributor.

20 THE LITTLE RED HEN

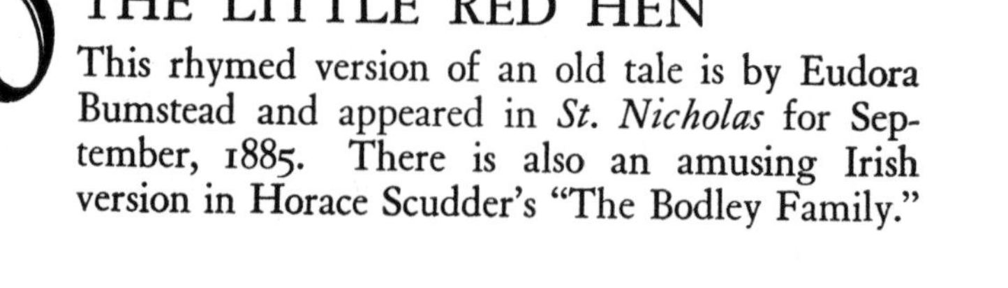

This rhymed version of an old tale is by Eudora Bumstead and appeared in *St. Nicholas* for September, 1885. There is also an amusing Irish version in Horace Scudder's "The Bodley Family."

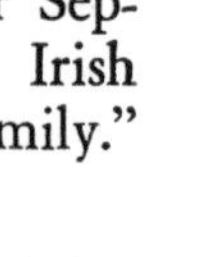

21 MR. BOURNE AND HIS WIFE

Anonymous. Sung to Julia Ward Howe in childhood by her uncle, Dr. John Wakefield Francis.

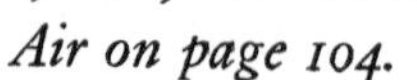

Air on page 104.

22 THE BUMBLE-BUG

Anonymous. Found in Horace Scudder's "Doings of the Bodley Family in Town and Country," (1875).

23 CLUCK, CLUCK

A nursery favorite of the 'seventies, contributed by "Fall River" who has long been known to readers of the *Boston Transcript* Notes and Queries Department as an expert searcher of old rhymes and lost lines.

Air on page 104.

24 RUFFLECUMTUFFLE

By Annette Bishop, probably about 1875. Contributed in entirety by "Fall River."

FOREWORD

MANY years ago a little girl—who was the youngest of seven brothers and sisters—took delight in songs and rhymes her mother used to sing at bedtime, or administer as balm and diversion of mind for childish stomach-aches and finger cuts. There was "Little Dame Crump" and "We're All Nodding," and the one we called "Oh, what shall the wedding supper be?" and "Go Tell Aunt Nabby." And there was "The Little Red Hen," remembered as especially entrancing from the lips of an older sister.

In later years I realized that these—and other nursery jingles and ballads—are an indescribably precious part of childhood which every child should possess. But I discovered that some of the rhymes I loved best were not contained in any book, and others were extremely hard to find. This led me to a fascinating search for rhymes that are traditional in the strict sense of having been transmitted by word of mouth from generation to generation. I also found others not so old—such as Eudora Bumsted's irresistible "Little Red Hen," written in 1855—that belong in this collection by virtue of having been said or sung by mothers in American homes for the joy of children for at least three generations. Most of the rhymes selected for this book have been rescued from the memories of older people, or from out-of-print books. In a few cases they have been taken from books not easily available to children.

I have included "Frog Went A-courting" and "The Keys of Heaven," which are comparatively well known and to be found in collections of old songs such as Cecil Sharp's "Nursery Songs From the Appalachian Mountains." I included them not only because they were special favorites of my childhood but because the elder sister who used to tell me "The Little Red Hen" had found and recorded these songs, as sung traditionally in the mountains of North Carolina, years before Cecil Sharp came to this country on his quest. "Frog Went A-courting" has literally hundreds of variants as remembered in hundreds of households, and I have chosen a version sung today by the children at Pine Mountain, Kentucky. I am indebted to Miss Gladys Atwell for these verses.

Another song included in spite of the fact that two stanzas of it are almost universally known, is "The Old Gray Goose." Of more than thirty versions of this song brought to light through an appeal in the Herald-Tribune "Readers' Guide," the version I have given, as sung by an old negro in Florida a generation ago and sent to me by Mr. P. R. Newell, is the longest. In my childhood I knew the bereaved owner of the goose as Aunt *Nabby,* and other versions call her Nancy, Dinah and Abby, but as two-thirds of the replies favored Rhody I have yielded to the stronger tradition.

The rhymes in this book have possibly been loved as genuinely as the shorter and more familiar Mother Goose Melodies, but because they have never had the multiple publication of Mother Goose, are not as widely known. Indeed, some of them have been in danger of being soon forgotten and lost forever.

I have refrained from including rhymes that can be found in complete editions of Mother Goose or in other anthologies of bygone favorites, although this meant omitting some of the special treasures of my childhood which appear in Esther Forbes' "Favorites of the Nursery Seventy Years Ago" and John Greenleaf Whittier's "Child Life in Poetry."

I am indebted chiefly to my mother for love of the songs and the singing that make childhood happy, and for the impulse to make this collection for children. But I am deeply indebted also to many people who have given me enthusiastic encouragement as well as contributions of remembered rhymes, in the years the collection has been in the making:

> To Wilbur Macey Stone, who allowed me to pore through dozens of the precious volumes of his distinguished collection of old children's books; To Laura E. Richards who contributed "Merry Green Fields of England," "The Old Crow," "Old Crummles" and "Mr. Bourne and His Wife,"—four songs which her mother, Julia Ward Howe sang to her. To Mary Barling Street who preserved for her children's delight "The Tragic Tale of Hooty the Owl" and the versions here used of "The Hungry Fox" and "The Keys of Heaven"; To Henry E. Fries, who allowed me to use from an early edition of "Mother Goose's Melodies" a rhyme which I have not found in any later edition; to the Notes and Queries Department of the Boston Transcript and the Readers' Guide of the New York Herald Tribune, and to their readers for invaluable assistance in producing from their memories certain of the rhymes which were hard to find in entirety.

The value of these old songs and rhymes is not likely to be questioned, I think, by anyone who has seen children enjoy them. As James Orchard Halliwell, the great collector of the oldest Mother Goose material, said in the preface to the 1853 edition of "The Nursery Rhymes of England": "The nursery rhyme is the novel and light reading of the infant scholar. It occupies, with respect to the ABC, the position of a romance which relieves the mind from the cares of a riper age. . . . The infants and children of the nineteenth century have not deserted the rhymes chanted so many ages since by the mothers of the north. This is a great nursery fact—a proof that there is contained in some of these traditional nonsense rhymes a meaning and a romance, possibly intelligible only to very young minds, that exercises an influence on the minds of children. It is obvious that there must exist something of this kind, for no modern competitors are found to supply altogether the place of ancient doggrel."

Much of the material in this book is not truly "ancient doggrel" but it is made of seasoned fun that has a natural appeal to children. Perhaps the only quality which unifies a collection which must, from a literary point of view, be considered rather motley, is the common possession of loveableness to children. Children have loved these poems and they have been passed down from mother to child as a heritage. They are the endeared lines which —repeated even for the hundredth time—have power to soothe ruffled spirits and make the world right again, even as "Where is my little basket gone?" had magic to cure a bump, in Habberton's classic story, and as "The Bumble Bug," in Horace Scudder's "Doings of the Bodley Family" was the ballad which little Nathan loved to have his mother repeat to him after he was tucked into bed at night, "though he had heard it a great many times."

In the Table of Contents, I have recaptured another joy of my childhood in using Kate Greenaway's device for illustrating the first pages of "Under the Window."

And so, with Robert Lawson's invaluable support I have put these blackbirds into a pie before they have flown away forever, with the hope that when the pie is opened they will sing both lustily and sweetly for American children.

HELEN DEAN FISH.

Sing a song of sixpence,
A bag full of rye;
Four-and-twenty blackbirds
Baked in a pie.

When the pie was opened,
The birds began to sing;
Was not that a dainty dish
To set before the king?

The king was in his counting-house
Counting out his money;
The queen was in the parlour,
Eating bread and honey;

The maid was in the garden,
Hanging out the clothes;
Down came a blackbird
And pecked off her nose.

FOUR AND TWENTY BLACKBIRDS

1

Little Dame Crump

OH, LITTLE Dame Crump with her little hair broom
One morning was sweeping her little bed room
When casting her little gray eyes on the ground
In a sly little corner a penny she found.

"*Odd-dobbs*," cried the maid, and she starts with surprise,
"How lucky I am; bless me heart, what a prize!
"To the market I'll go and a pig I will buy
"And little John Gubbins shall build him a sty."

So she washed her face clean and put on her gown
And locked up her house and started for town.
To market she went and a bargain she made,
And for little white piggie a penny she paid.

Now the bargain was made she was puzzled to know
    How they both should get home, as the pig would not go.
So fearing that piggie might play her a trick,
    She drove him along with a little crab stick.

Piggie ran till he came to the foot of the hill
    Where a little bridge crosses a stream from the mill,
There he grunted and squealed and no further would go.
    Oh, fie, little piggie to serve poor dame so!

She went into the mill and borrowed a sack
    Popped in the pig and took him on her back.
Piggie squealed to get out, but the little dame said,
    "If you can't go by fair means, then you must be made."

She soon to the end of the journey did come
    She was mightily pleased to get piggie home.
She carried him right to his nice little sty,
    And made him a bed of straw clean and dry.

With a handful of pease poor piggie she fed;
    She popped on her nightcap and hopped into bed.
Having first said her prayers, she blew out the light,
    And being quite tired, we'll bid her goodnight.

·2·

Merry Green Fields of England

MY GRANDFATHER had two very fine hens,
Merry green fields of England!
With a kickle cackle here,
And a kickle cackle there,
Here a kickle, there a cackle,
Here and there a kickle cackle,
Hi for the next one,
Come along with me,
Merry green fields of England!

My grandfather had two very fine ducks,
    Merry green fields of England!
With a quack quack here,
And a quack quack there,
Here a quack, there a quack,
Here and there a quack, quack,
    Hi for the next one,
    Come along with me,
    Merry green fields of England!

My grandfather had two very fine geese,
    Merry green fields of England!
With a gabble gabble here,
And a gabble gabble there,
Here a gabble, there a gabble,
Here and there a gabble gabble,
    Hi for the next one,
    Come along with me,
    Merry green fields of England!

My grandfather had two very fine turkeys,
    Merry green fields of England!
With a gobble gobble here,
And a gobble gobble there,
Here a gobble, there a gobble,
Here and there a gobble gobble,
    Hi for the next one,
    Come along with me,
    Merry green fields of England!

My grandfather had two very fine dogs,
    Merry green fields of England!
With a bow wow here,
And a bow wow there,
Here a bow, and there a wow,
Here and there a bow wow,
    Hi for the next one,
    Come along with me,
    Merry green fields of England!

My grandfather had two very fine cats,
    Merry green fields of England!
With a miaow miaow here,
And a miaow miaow there,
Here a miaow, there a miaow,
Here and there a miaow miaow,
    Hi for the next one,
    Come along with me,
    Merry green fields of England!

My grandfather had two very fine sheep,
    Merry green fields of England!
With a baa baa here,
And a baa baa there,
Here a baa, there a baa,
Here and there a baa baa,
    Hi for the next one,
    Come along with me,
    Merry green fields of England!

My grandfather had two very fine cows,
    Merry green fields of England!
With a moo moo here,
And a moo moo there,
Here a moo, there a moo,
Here and there a moo moo,
    Hi for the next one,
    Come along with me,
    Merry green fields of England!

My grandfather had two very fine donkeys,
    Merry green fields of England!
With a hee hee here,
And a haw haw there,
Here a hee, there a haw,
Here and there a hee haw,
    Hi for the next one,
    Come along with me,
    Merry green fields of England!

My grandfather had two very fine pigs,
    Merry green fields of England!
With a hunk hunk here,
And a hunk hunk there,
Here a hunk, there a hunk,
Here and there a hunk hunk,
    Hi for the next one,
    Come along with me,
    Merry green fields of England!

·3·

The Old Gray Goose

GO TELL Aunt Rhody, go tell Aunt Rhody,
Go tell Aunt Rhody, her old gray goose is dead.

The one she was saving, the one she was saving,
The one she was saving to make a feather bed.

She died in the haystack, died in the haystack,
Died in the haystack with a toothache in her head.

The barnyard is mourning, the barnyard is mourning,
The barnyard is mourning and waiting to be fed.

We'll bury her at daybreak, bury her at daybreak,
Bury her at daybreak, just like Aunt Rhody said.

Then we'll all join the chorus, the grave is before us,
'Twas dug with a shovel by old Uncle Ned.

We'll eat no more goose eggs, eat no more goose eggs,
Eat no more goose eggs, 'cause the old gray goose is dead.

◆4◆

The Robber Kitten

A KITTEN once to its mother said,
"I'll never more be good;
But I'll go and be a robber fierce,
And live in a dreary wood!
Wood! Wood! Wood!
And live in a dreary wood!"

So off it went to the dreary wood,
And there it met a cock
And blew its head, with a pistol, off
Which gave it an awful shock!
Shock! Shock! Shock!
Which gave it an awful shock!

It climbed a tree to rob a nest
Of young and tender owls;
But the branch broke off, and the kitten fell,
With six tremendous howls!
Howls! Howls! Howls!
With six tremendous howls!

Soon after that it met a cat:
"Now give to me your purse;
Or I'll shoot you through and stab you too,
And kill you which is worse!
Worse! Worse! Worse!
And kill you which is worse!"

One day it met a robber dog
And they sat down to drink;
The dog did joke and laugh and sing,
Which made the kitten wink!
Wink! Wink! Wink!
Which made the kitten wink!

At last they quarreled: then they fought
Beneath the greenwood tree,
Till puss was felled with an awful club.
Most terrible to see!
See! See! See!
Most terrible to see!

RL

When puss got up, its eye was shut,
And swelled and black and blue;
Moreover, all its bones were sore;
So it began to mew!
Mew! Mew! Mew!
So it began to mew!

Then up it rose and scratched its nose,
And went home very sad:
"Oh, mother dear! Behold me here,
I'll never more be bad!
Bad! Bad! Bad!
"I'll never more be bad!"

·5·

The Ragman

THERE was a ragman and a madman
Dwelt together in a barn,
And a peddler and a fiddler
Stole away the ragman's horn
But the ragman made the madman
Give the peddler such a bang
That the peddler made the fiddler
Give him back his horn again.

· 6 ·

Joe Dobson

JOE DOBSON was an Englishman
In days of Robin Hood
A country farmer eke was he
In Forest of Sherwood.

Joe Dobson said unto his Dame
I vow that I could do
More household work in any day
Than you could do in two.

She e'en replied, I do declare
Your words you shall fulfil
Tomorrow you my place shall take
I'll do the plow and mill.

Next morning came, they sallied forth
Each sure of doing well
She with her stick, he with a pail
The rest I soon will tell.

Away went Joe to milk the cow
His business to begin.
She tossed the pail and kicked his leg
And blood ran down his shin.

But see him now sit down to reel
The yarn his rib had spun.
But puzzled and perplexed was he
And swore it was no fun.

Next job to boil the pot he went
The fire he had forgot!
He ran with chips and burnt his head,
Oh, grievous was his lot.

Away went Joe to wash the cloathes
But sore against his will
The water scalded both his hands
Bad luck pursued him still.

He went to hang the cloathes to dry
It was a lovely day
But oh, alas, a magpie came
And stole his wig away.

Away went Dobson in despair
At losing thus his wig
The magpie flew with rapid flight
And left it on a twig.

Good lack, quoth he, I must dispatch
And haste the bread to make
But stooping down to knead it well
His back did sorely ache.

Loud crowed the cocks, the turkeys screamed
The geese and ducks now quacked
Enraged for food which Joe forgot
He was by all attacked.

An effort then poor Dobson made
The little pigs to feed
The old sow tripped him in the mud
In spite of all his heed.

The old Dame now with speed returned
Quite stout and blithe was she
And found poor Joe all bruised and ill
Fatigued as he could be.

Now Mrs. Dobson, tidy soul,
Soon set all neat and right.
Prepared the meat and drew the ale.
They bravely fared that night.

Whilst they partook this dainty meal
Joe suddenly confessed
He was convinced that wives could do
The household business best.

7

Poor Lady Dumpling

POOR Lady Dumpling,
Poor Lady Dumpling,
She grew so fat and big
She couldn't ride in coach or cars
Or even in a gig.
So round she had to trot,
Till on a summer's day
The sun came out so hot,
She melted all away.

RL

·8·

Old Mother Tabbyskins

SITTING at her window in her cloak and hat,
I saw Mother Tabbyskins, the real old cat;
Very old, very old, crumplety and lame,
Teaching kittens how to scold–is it not a shame?

Kittens in the garden, looking in her face,
Learning how to spit and scold—eh, what a disgrace!
Very wrong, very wrong—very wrong and bad;
Such a subject for our song makes us all too sad.

Old Mother Tabbyskins sticking out her head,
Gave a howl and then a yowl and hobbled off to bed.
Very sick, very sick! Very savage too!
Pray send for a doctor quick! any one will do.

Doctor Mouse came creeping, creeping to her bed,
Lanced her gums and felt her pulse—whispered she was dead.
Very sly, very sly, the real old cat
Open kept her weather eye—Mouse, beware of that!

Old Mother Tabbyskins, saying "Serves him right,"
Gobbled up the doctor with infinite delight.
"Very fast, very fast! very pleasant too!
What a pity it can't last—bring another, do!"

Doctor Dog comes running—just to see her begs;
Round his neck a comforter, trousers on his legs.
Very grand! very grand! golden headed cane
Swinging gayly from his hand, mischief in his brain.

"Dear Mother Tabbyskins, and how are you now?
Let me feel your pulse—so, so! show your tongue—bow-wow!
Very ill, very ill! Please attempt to purr!
Will you take a draught or pill—which do you prefer?"

Ah, Mother Tabbyskins, who is now afraid?
Of poor little Doctor Mouse you a mouthful made.
Very nice, very nice little doctor he!
But for Doctor Dog's advice *you* must pay the fee.

Doctor Dog comes nearer—says she must be bled.
I heard Mother Tabbyskins screaming in her bed.
Very near, very near! scuffling out and in,
Doctor Dog looks full and queer. Where is Tabbyskin?

I will tell the moral without any fuss:
Those who lead the young astray always suffer thus.
Very nice, very nice let our conduct be,
For all doctors are not mice; some are dogs you see!

9

The Hungry Fox

A FOX went out in a hungry plight
And he begged of the moon to give him some light
For he had many miles to travel that night
Before he reached his den–O.

He ran till he came to the farmer's yard
Where the ducks and the geese declared it hard
That their sleep should be broken and their rest should be marred
By a visit from Mr. Fox–O.

He took the gray goose by the neck
And he slung her right across his back.
And the old goose cried out, "Quack! Quack! Quack!"
With her legs hanging dangling down–O.

Old Mrs. Slipper-slopper jumped out of bed,
And out of the window she popped her head,
Crying, "John! John! John!" the gray goose is gone,
And the Fox is off to his den–O!"

Then John he went to the top of the hill,
And he blew a blast both loud and shrill.
Said the fox, "That is very pretty music, still
I'd rather be off to my den–O."

At last the fox got home to his den,
To his dear little foxes, eight, nine, ten,
Said he, "You're in luck, here's a fine fat duck,
With his legs hanging dangling down–O."

Then the fox sat down with his hungry wife,
And they did very well without fork or knife,
They never ate a better duck in all their life,
And the little ones picked the bones–O.

·10·

Frog Went A-Courting

FROG went a-courting, he did ride, a-hum, a-hum,
Frog went a-courting, he did ride,
Sword and pistol by his side, a-hum, a-hum.

He rode till he came to Miss Mouse's Hall, a-hum, a-hum,
He rode till he came to Miss Mouse's Hall,
He gave a loud knock and he gave a loud call, a-hum, a-hum.

Said he, "Miss Mouse, are you within?" a-hum, a-hum,
Said he, "Miss Mouse, are you within?"
"Yes, kind sir, I'm sitting to spin," a-hum, a-hum.

He took Miss Mouse upon his knee, a-hum, a-hum,
He took Miss Mouse upon his knee,
And said, "Miss Mouse, will you marry me?" a-hum, a-hum.

"Oh, not without Uncle Rat's consent," a-hum, a-hum,
"Not without Uncle Rat's consent,
Would I marry the President," a-hum, a-hum.

Uncle Rat laughed till he shook his fat sides, a-hum, a-hum,
Uncle Rat laughed till he shook his fat sides
To think that his niece would soon be a bride, a-hum, a-hum.

Oh, where will the wedding supper be? a-hum, a-hum,
Where will the wedding supper be?
Down in the hollow of the old oak tree, a-hum, a-hum.

Oh, what will the wedding supper be? a-hum, a-hum,
What will the wedding supper be?
A slice of bread and a cup of tea, a-hum, a-hum.

The first to come was a little moth, a-hum, a-hum,
The first to come was a little moth,
To spread on the table cloth, a-hum, a-hum.

The next came in was a bumble bee, a-hum, a-hum,
The next came in was a bumble bee
With his fiddle on his knee, a-hum, a-hum.

The next came in was a nimble flea, a-hum, a-hum,
The next came in was a nimble flea
To take a jig with the bumble bee, a-hum, a-hum.

The next came in was a little old fly, a-hum, a-hum,
The next came in was a little old fly,
He ate up all the wedding pie, a-hum, a-hum.

The next came in was a little old chick, a-hum, a-hum,
The next came in was a little old chick,
He ate so much that it made him sick, a-hum, a-hum.

The next came in was an old tom-cat, a-hum, a-hum,
The next came in was an old tom-cat,
He swallowed Miss Mouse as slick as a rat, a-hum, a-hum.

Gentleman Frog swam over the lake, a-hum, a-hum,
Gentleman Frog swam over the lake,
And he got swallowed by a big black snake, a-hum, a-hum.

So here is the end of one, two, three, a-hum, a-hum,
So here is the end of one, two, three,
The frog and the mouse and the bumble bee, a-hum, a-hum, ***a-hum.***

·11·

The Keys of Heaven

"I'LL give to you a paper of pins
For that's the way true love begins,
If you will marry me, me, me,
If you will marry me!"

"I don't want your paper of pins
If that's the way that love begins,
And I won't marry you, you, you,
And I won't marry you!"

"I'll give to you a dress of red,
Stitched all round with a golden thread,
If you will marry me, me, me,
If you will marry me."

"I don't want your dress of red,
Stitched all round with a golden thread,
And I won't marry you, you, you,
And I won't marry you!"

"I'll give to you a dress of green,
That you may look as fine as a queen,
If you will marry me, me, me,
If you will marry me."

"I don't want your dress of green
That I may look as fine as a queen,
And I won't marry you, you, you,
And I won't marry you."

"I'll give to you a house and land,
That you may have at your command,
If you will marry me, me, me,
If you will marry me."

"I don't want your house and land
That I may have at my command,
And I won't marry you, you, you,
And I won't marry you."

"I'll give to you the key to my heart
That we may marry and never part,
If you will marry me, me, me,
If you will marry me."

RL

"I don't want the key of your heart,
That we may marry and never part,
And I won't marry you, you, you,
And I won't marry you."

"I'll give to you the key of my chest
That you may have money at your request
If you will marry me, me, me,
If you will marry me."

"I will take the key of your chest
That I may have money at my request
And I will marry you, you, you,
And I will marry you."

"You love coffee and I love tea,
You love my money but you don't love me,
And I'll not marry you, Miss, you,
And I'll not marry you!"

·12·

Dame Trot and Her Comical Cat

OLD Dame Trot
  Set off to the fair,
With her cat on her shoulder,
  To see the folks there.
The people all laughed
  As they saw them go by:
Says the Dame, "I'll laugh too,"
  But says Pussy, "I'll cry."

She bought her some shoes
  Of a very bright red:
But when she came back,
  She found Pussy in bed.
She went to the cloak-shop
  And bought her a cloak:
When she came back again
  Pussy just had woke.

She went to the dairy
To buy her some milk:
When she came back
Puss was sewing on silk.
She went to the fish-shop
And bought her some fish:
When she came back,
Puss was washing a dish.

She went to the florist's
To buy her a rose:
When she came back,
Pussy stood on her nose.
She went to the fruit-shop
To buy her a plum:
When she came back,
Puss was beating a drum.

She went to the miller's
To grind her some corn:
When she came back
Puss was blowing a horn.
She went to the upholsterer's
To buy a new bed;
But while she was out
Naughty Pussy had fled.

RL

She went out again
    And from a man from the fair,
She bought for herself
    A nice rush-bottomed chair.
She went out the next time
    To buy Pussy a hat:
When she came back
    Puss was catching a rat.

She went to the baker's,
    To buy her a bun:
When she came back
    Puss was loading a gun.
She went to the grocer's
    To buy her some figs:
When she came back
    Puss was feeding the pigs.

She went to the butcher's
    For meat, I suppose,
When she came back
    Puss was washing some clothes.
She next bought some fur,
    And a dress of sky-blue;
Says Dame Trot, "Say 'Thank you' ";
    But Pussy said, "Mew!"

·13·

The Old Crow

YONDER is an old crow sitting on an oak
With a ring ting meloding kimo.
Yonder is a tailor a-sewing on a cloak,
With a ring ting meloding kimo.
Oh, wife, oh wife, come bring me my bow,
With a ring ting meloding kimo,
That I may shoot yon carrion crow,
With a ring ting meloding kimo.

Chorus: *Kimo lera, kimo lera,*
Kummerummer, kummerummer,
Kimo lera,
With a ring ting, meloding kimo.

The tailor shot but he missed his mark,
With a ring ting meloding kimo,
And he shot his old sow right through the heart,
With a ring ting meloding kimo.
Oh wife, oh wife, oh ring the bell,
With a ring ting meloding kimo,
That I may bid my sow farewell,
With a ring ting meloding kimo.

Chorus: *Kimo lera, kimo lera,*
Kummerummer, kummerummer,
Kimo lera,
With a ring ting, meloding kimo.

And when the bell began to ring,
With a ring ting meloding kimo,
The little pigs marched in deep mourning,
With a ring ting meloding kimo,
And when the bell began to toll,
With a ring ting meloding kimo,
The little pigs prayed for the old sow's soul,
With a ring ting meloding kimo.

Chorus: *Kimo lera, kimo lera,*
Kummerummer, kummerummer,
Kimo lera,
With a ring ting, meloding kimo.

14

Come Hither

COME hither, little puppy dog;
I'll give you a new collar,
If you will learn to read your book
And be a clever scholar.
No, no! replied the puppy dog,
I've other fish to fry,
For I must learn to guard your house,
And bark when thieves come nigh.
With a tingle, tangle, tit-mouse!
Robin knows great A,
And B, and C, and D, and E, F, G
H, I, J, K.

Come hither, pretty cockatoo;
Come and learn your letters;
And you shall have a knife and fork
To eat with, like your betters.
No, no! the cockatoo replied,
My beak will do as well;
I'd rather eat my victuals thus
Than go and learn to spell.

With a tingle, tangle, tit-mouse!
Robin knows great A,
And B, and C, and D, and E, F, G,
H, I, J, K.

Come hither, little pussy cat;
If you'll your grammar study
I'll give you silver clogs to wear,
When e'er the gutter's muddy.
No! whilst I grammar learn, says Puss,
Your house will in a trice
Be overrun from top to bottom
With flocks of rats and mice.

With a tingle, tangle, tit-mouse!
Robin knows great A,
And B, and C, and D, and E, F, G,
H, I, J, K.

Come hither, then, good little boy,
And learn your alphabet,
And you a pair of boots and spurs,
Like your papa's, shall get.
Oh, yes! I'll learn my alphabet;
And when I well can read,
Perhaps papa will give, me, too,
A pretty long-tailed steed.

With a tingle, tangle, tit-mouse!
Robin knows great A,
And B, and C, and D, and E, F, G,
H, I, J, K, L, M, N, O, P, Q, R, S,
T, U, V, W, X, Y, Z.

· 15 ·

Old Crummles

OLD Crummles is dead and laid in his grave,
Oh, ho! laid in his grave!
There grew an old appletree over his grave,
Oh, ho! over his grave!
The apples were ripe and ready to drop,
Oh, ho! ready to drop!
There came an old woman a-picking them up,
Oh, ho! picking them up!
Old Crummles arose and gave her a slap,
Oh, ho! gave her a slap!
Which made the old woman go flippity-flap,
Oh, ho! flippity-flap!
He hinched her, he pinched her, he made her back smart,
Oh, ho! made her back smart!
If ever we catch him we'll cut out his heart,
Oh, ho! chop out his heart!

RL

So they hopped away to Strawberry Hill.
Oh, ho! Strawberry Hill!
And there they sat down while she made her a will,
Oh, ho! made her a will!
My best wedding shoon to yon lady so fair,
Oh, ho! lady so fair!
But 'tis Johnny Cahoon that shall have the gray mare,
Oh, ho! have the gray mare!
The saddle and bridle are laid on the shelf,
Oh, ho! laid on the shelf!
If you want any more you may sing it yourself,
Oh, ho! sing it yourself!

16

Jim Finley's Pig

OLD Jim Finley had a little pig
Uh-huh, uh-huh
Old Jim Finley had a little pig
It was so little that it niver grew big
Uh-huh, uh-huh.

He put his piggie in a sty
Uh-huh, uh-huh
He put his piggie in a sty
The old woman she stood by and by
Uh-huh, uh-huh.

The old woman, she went to feed the pig
Uh-huh, uh-huh
The old woman she went to feed the pig,
And when she got there the piggie was dead
Uh-huh, uh-huh.

The old woman she grieved herself to death
Uh-huh, uh-huh
The old woman she grieved herself to death
Because little piggie had lost his breath
Uh-huh, uh-huh.

The old man he died soon arter
Uh-huh, uh-huh
The old man he died soon arter
He hung himself with his garter
Uh-huh, uh-huh.

So this is the end of one, two, three,
Uh-huh, uh-huh
So this is the end of one, two, three
The old man, woman and the little pig-gie
Uh-huh, uh-huh.

The ancient book lies on the shelf
Uh-huh, uh-huh
The ancient book lies on the shelf
If you want any more you can sing it yourself
Uh-huh, uh-huh.

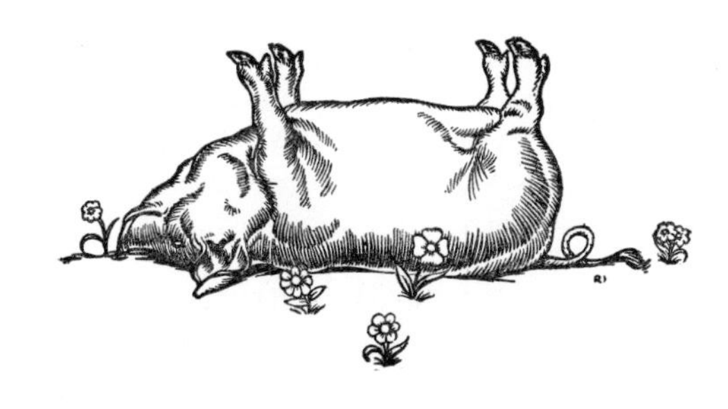

·17·

We Are All Nodding

WE ARE all nodding, nid, nid, nodding,
We are all nodding
At our house at home.
With a turning in and a turning out,
And it's this way, that way, round about,
We are all nodding, nid, nid, nodding
We are all nodding,
At our house at home.

We are all sewing, sew, sew, sewing
We are all sewing
At our house at home.
With a turning in and a turning out,
And it's this way, that way, round about,
We are all sewing, sew, sew, sewing,
We are all sewing
At our house at home.

We are all fiddling, fid, fid, fiddling,
  We are all fiddling
  At our house at home.
With a turning in and a turning out,
And it's this way, that way, round about,
We are all fiddling, fid, fid, fiddling
  We are all fiddling
  At our house at home.

We are all reading, read, read, reading,
  We are all reading
  At our house at home.
With a turning in and a turning out,
And it's this way, that way, round about,
We are all reading, read, read, reading
  We are all reading
  At our house at home.

We are all spinning, spin, spin, spinning,
  We are all spinning
  At our house at home.
With a turning in and a turning out,
And it's this way, that way, round about,
We are all spinning, spin, spin, spinning
  We are all spinning
  At our house at home.

18

The Tragic Tale of Hooty the Owl

THERE was once an old fox
    Who lived under the rocks
At the foot of a huge old tree,
    And of all the foxes who ever did live
There was none so bad as he.

His step was soft with his padded feet
    But his claws were sharp beneath,
And sharper his eyes and sharper his ears,
    And sharper his terrible teeth.

The dreariest place you ever did see
Was this old fox's den—
It was clothed with the down of the tender chick
And the wing of the matron hen.

There was an owl lived at the top of the tree. This owl was named Hooty, and often at night, when loudly the night wind blew, he would watch the old fox in the hole in the rocks with a, "Whit-too-Whit-too-Whoo!"

Then the owl would laugh at the top of the tree
To hear him wake and growl—
For he hated the fox who lived under the rocks
And the fox he hated the owl.

Now the owl had a little son, Billy by name,
    And a beautiful owlet was he.
His eyes were as big as the lamps of a gig
    And his bill was a wonder to see.

He never cried when his hair was combed
    Nor screamed when they wiped his nose
Nor washed his face and got soap in his eyes
    And he never soiled his clothes.

Wasn't he a good little owl?

But as good as he was, his father had a great deal of trouble making him stay in the hole. One day Hooty had to go away and as he was going he said to his son:

"Now, Bill, I command and beseech you,
    Don't leave the nest is my earnest request,
For the old fox may catch you and eat you.
    He is watching below to catch you, I know,
So don't try to fly till I teach you."

"Mayn't I go out on the big bough?"

"No, Billy."

"Just a little way?" said Billy.

"Now, William," said the old owl, "you know I am mild but firm. If I hear any more of this, I will turn back your tail feathers and give you a spanking you will remember. Do you hear me?"

And Billy said, "Yes, sir."

When Hooty had gone the old fox came out and called, "Billy!"

And Billy said, "What?"

"Come down and play with me. I love little owls." (And so he did, the bad old fox!)

"Oh, no, Father said I must not."

"Never mind what your father said. Come down and play with me. I love little owls."

So poor little Billy was so very silly
He climbed out on the bough.
And the old fox laughed with a "Ha-ha-ha!"
And whispered, "I've got you now!"

And Billy tried to fly and fell down on the ground, and the old fox picked him up.

"Oh, Mr. Fox, please, Mr. Fox, don't eat me!"

"Yes, I will," said the fox, "I love little owls." And he bit off his head and sucked his blood and ate him all up, and then he lay down to see what Hooty would do when he came back.

At last he heard a flapping of wings
And Hooty lit on a tree.
His screams were wild when he sought his child
And Billy, nowhere was he.

And he laid him down in his empty nest
And covered his face with his wing
And big sobs came from his speckled breast
And he cried like anything.

And he screamed so loud in his wrath and woe
That he shook the huge old tree,
And the old fox heard him as he lay below
And he laughed, "Ha-ha, he-he!"

Then Hooty stopped crying and wiped his eyes,
And shook his fist at the fox.
"You naughty villain, you stole my child
And carried him under the rocks."

"You've eaten my Billy, my pretty first-born,
Without any equal for beauty.
But I'll tell Jack with his hounds and his horn
As sure as my name is Hooty.

"And the bow-wow dogs and the toot-toot horns
And the galloping horse and Jack
Will race you and chase you wherever they trace you
And scramble along your track.

"And I will think of my Billy that's dead
As I flap along your trail
And see the dogs bite off your cruel head
And Jack ride away with your tail."

So Hooty went to where Jack lived and told him where the fox lived and Jack said, "I'll come and catch him for he is the very fox that killed the cock that crowed in the morn."

So soon in the morning out went Jack
With his spurs on his heels and his whip to crack
And he saddled his horse and called to his pack
And started out on the fox's track.

Away he went on the frosty ground
    With the deep, deep bay of the hound.

The fox had been out to get a goose for his dinner and hid in a hollow tree. And there he was with his tongue hanging out and gasping for breath, and froth on his lips, but game to the death.

He fought and fought the dogs till he died,
    He bit Growler's foot and cut Tray's side.
They tore him in pieces, no mercy he begs,
    But some of the dogs limped home on three legs.

And Jack came and cut off his tail
    And carried it home to hang on a nail.
For this was the fox that Jack would tell
    That ran so far and fought so well.

And the owl looked down from the branch overhead
    Where the lifeless, tailless fox lay dead,
And laughed aloud as away he flew,
    "Too-whit, too-whit, too-whit, too-whoo!"

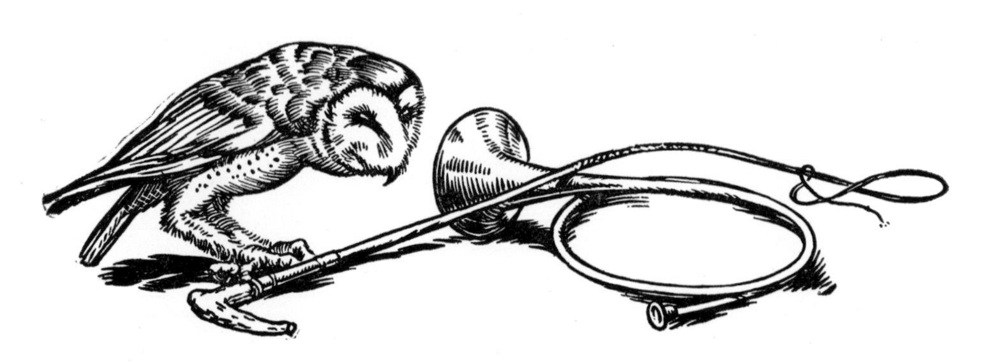

19

The Two Foxes

ON A winter's night
When the moon shone bright,
Two foxes went out for their prey;
As they trotted along
With frolic and song
They cheered the lonely way.

Through the woods they went
But they could not scent
A rabbit or goose astray,
Till at length they came
To some better game
In a farmer's barn by the way.

On the roost, there sat
Some chickens as fat
As foxes could wish for their dinners
So the prowlers found
A hole in the ground
And both went in, the sinners!

They both went in
With a squeeze and a grin;
And the chickens were quickly killed
And one of them munched
And feasted and lunched,
Till his stomach was fairly filled.

The other, more wise,
Looked about with both eyes
And scarcely did eat at all;
For as he came in
With a squeeze and a grin
He remarked that the hole was small.

Thus matters went on
Till the night was gone,
And the farmer came out with a pole.
Both foxes flew,
And one got through,
But the greedy one stuck in the hole.

In the hole he stuck,
So full was his pluck,
Of the chickens he had been eating.
He could neither get out
Nor turn about,
And so he was killed by beating.

And thus, you see
So greedy was he
He died for a single dinner;
And I hope that you
Will believe this true
And never be such a sinner.

20

The Little Red Hen

LITTLE Red Hen looked busily round
In search of a bit to eat,
Till hid in the straw and chaff, she found
A plump little grain of wheat.

"Now who will plant this wheat?" she cried.
"Not I!" the Goose and the Duck replied;
"Not I!" said the Dog and the Cat;
"Not I!" said the Mouse and the Rat.

"Oh, I will, then!" said the Little Red Hen,
And scratched with her quick little feet,
Till a hole she dug, and covered it snug,
And so she planted the wheat.

Little Red Hen gave tender care;
The rain and the shine came down,
And the wheat grew green and tall and fair,
Then turned to a golden brown.

"Now who will reap this wheat?" she cried,
"Not I!" the Goose and the Duck replied.
"Not I!" said the Dog and the Cat;
"Not I!" said the Mouse and the Rat.

"Oh, I will, then," said the Little Red Hen;
And braving the midsummer heat,
She cut it at will with her trim little bill
And so she reaped the wheat.

Little Red Hen peeped slyly about
From her snug little nest in the hay;
If only that wheat were all threshed out
And fit to be stored away!

"Now who will thresh this wheat?" she cried,
"Not I!" the Goose and the Duck replied.
"Not I!" said the Dog and the Cat;
"Not I!" said the Mouse and the Rat.

"Oh, I will, then," said the Little Red Hen
And having no flail, she beat
With her wings of red on the grain, instead,
And so she threshed the wheat.

Little Red Hen had still no rest
Although she had worked so well;
She thought of the chicks in her snug little nest
How soon they would peep in the shell.

"Now who will go to the mill?" she cried,
"Not I!" the Goose and the Duck replied.
"Not I!" said the Dog and the Cat;
"Not I!" said the Mouse and the Rat.

"Oh, I will, then," said the Little Red Hen,
And fashioned a sack so neat,
With corn-silk thread and a corn-husk red
In which she carried the wheat.

Little Red Hen then made some bread,
That was white and light and sweet,
And when it was done, she smiled and said,
"We'll see who is willing to eat."

"Now, who will eat this loaf?" she cried,
"I will!" the Goose and the Duck replied;
"I will!" said the Dog and the Cat;
"I will!" said the Mouse and the Rat.

"No doubt!" said the Hen, "if you get it!" and then
(How the lazy rogues longed for the treat!)
She clucked to her chicks—she was mother of six—
And that was the end of the wheat.

·21·

Mr. Bourne and His Wife

MR. BOURNE and his wife
One evening had a strife;
He wanted bread and butter with his tea;
But she swore she'd rule the roost
And she'd have a piece of toast,
So to loggerheads with him went she, she, she,
So to loggerheads with him went she.

Now there was a Mr. Moore
Lived on the second floor,
A man very strong in the wrist;
He overheard the splutter
About toast and bread and butter,
And he knocked down Mr. Bourne with his fist, fist, fist,
And he knocked down Mr. Bourne with his fist.

Quoth Moore, "By my life,
You shall not beat your wife!
It is both a sin and a disgrace!"
"You fool," said Mrs. Bourne,
" 'Tis no business of yourn!"
And she dashed a cup of tea in his face, face, face,
And she dashed a cup of tea in his face.

Quoth poor Mr. Moore,
As he sneaked to the door,
"I'm clearly an ass without brains:
For when married folks are flouting,
If a stranger pokes his snout in,
He is sure to get it tweaked for his pains, pains, pains,
He is sure to get it tweaked for his pains."

22

The Famous Battle of Bumble-Bug and Bumble-Bee

BUMBLE-BUG and Bumble-Bee
Agreed to fight a battle
For Bumble-Bug said Bumble-Bee
Had lighted on his apple.
So Bumble-Bug to Bumble-Bee
Cried out, "Come, sir, right down,
Or I will take you on my horns,
And toss you out of town."

But Bumble-Bee told Bumble-Bug
Apples were his to eat,
And bade the Buggy get away
With all his ugly feet.
Then Bumble-Bug began to swell
And Bumble-Bee to buzz,
And soon they had their little heads
All in a little fuzz.

And Bumble-Bug began to climb
The apple round and red,
And as he went a-bugging up
To Bumble-Bee he said,
"I'll show you, sir, old Bumble-Bee,
Whose apple you are eating;
I'll push you off upon the ground
And give you, sir, a beating."

Then Bumble-Bug and Bumble-Bee
Begin their famous battle
And soon both tumble headlong down
From off the big red apple.
But Bumble-Bug soon scrabbles up
And opens wide his eyes;
And Bumble-Bee shakes out his wings
And at Sir Buggy flies.

The Bumble-Bug tried hard to scratch,
The Bumble-Bee to sting;
The Bee put out the Buggy's eye,
The Bug tore off Bee's wing.
Then Bumble-Bug and Bumble-Bee
Each took a little rest
Sir Bug laid down upon his back,
Sir Bee upon his breast.

"Come, Bumble-Bug," said Bumble-Bee,
"Let's talk this matter over,
As we are resting here a bit
Under this shady clover."
" 'Twas all your fault!" cried Bumble-Bug;
" 'Twas yours!" cried Bumble-Bee;
"I found the apple first," said Bug,
"Under the apple tree."

"Ah, ha! ah ha!" cried Bumble-Bee
"Just like a great black bug!
I'll warrant you from out the ground
Your dinner oft have dug.
But I—*I* found the apple
Upon the apple tree;
I get my dinner clean and sweet,
I am a Bumble-Bee."

The Bumble-Bug said he'd get up
And kill the Bee outright
And Bumble-Bee began to buzz
All ready for the fight.
Oh, 'twas a fearful sight to see
As Bug with lifted horns
Went dash with all his might at Bee
With great black shiny horns!

Just then a tiny Ant spoke out,
From off her little hill,
And said, "Alas, most noble sirs,
My heart with grief you fill.
To see a Bumble-Bee and Bug
As like as any brothers
Go scratch and sting at eye and wing
Till each has spoiled the other's.

"The apple, big and red and round,
Is sure enough for all,
'Twould last a little Ant like me
The summer and the fall.
There Bumble-Bee could sip the juice
While Buggy nibbed the skin
And I, with hundred other Ants
Could tid-bit out and in.

“ ’Tis yours, ’tis mine; behold how fair
With wealth for each untold—
This rounded sphere of juicy pulp,
This rind of red and gold!
How pleasant too, as we have read,
How good a thing ’twould be.
Together as a family
To dwell in unity!”

Then Bumble-Bug and Bumble-Bee
Were very much ashamed
While thus the quiet little Ant
Their wicked conduct blamed;
And tears stood in that flashing eye
Down drooped that vaunting wing
As each pledged each to nevermore
Do such a naughty thing.

But not the tear in Buggy’s eye
Nor Bumble’s drooping wing,
Can take from out their little hearts
Remembered scratch and sting.
And ever, when they meet again,
On pretty fruit or flower
They think with still repenting hearts
Upon that battle hour.

·23·

Cluck, Cluck

THE hen to herself said one beautiful day,
"Cluck, cluck.
The day is so fine, I'll step over the way,
Cluck, cluck.
And call on my neighbor and friend Madam Duck,
Who lives on the opposite side of the brook,
Cluck, cluck, cluck, cluck, cluck, cluck."

So, smoothing her feathers, she called to her chicks,
"Cluck, cluck."
And bade them be sure to keep in her tracks,
Cluck, cluck.
For having no one to attend them at home,
She had to take them when abroad she did roam,
Cluck, cluck, cluck, cluck, cluck, cluck.

"Good day, Madam Hen," said the duck with a bow,
"Quack, quack!
I hope you are well and your dear chickens too,
Quack, quack.
And now let them go with my ducklings and play,
While we have a chat on the news of the day,
Quack, quack, quack, quack, quack, quack!"

So off went the chickens and ducklings to play,
Peep, peep.
And straight to the brook the young ducks led the way,
Peep, peep.
Right into the water they went without fear,
And called to the chickens to follow them there,
Peep, peep, peep, peep, peep, peep.

The ducklings so easily swam all about,
Peep, peep,
The chickens said, "Surely 'tis easy to float,
Peep, peep."
So in they all went, but alas, they soon found
That chicks are not ducks for the brood were all drowned.
Peep, peep, peep, peep, peep, peep.

·24·

Rufflecumtuffle

RUFFLECUMTUFFLE and Floppyfly,
Bibbetybobble and Kickittygo
Were four queer elves
Who lived by themselves
On a mountain high
And scorned the fairies that lived below.

But Rufflecumtuffle was a real dandy
With whiskers flowing wide and sandy;
And had wonderful wings
Painted with gold and scarlet rings;
And he longed to dance in the fairies' hall
For he knew he must outshine them all.

So Rufflecumtuffle decided to go,
And he did not mean the others to know.
        He sought for a steed
        To take him down the mountain with speed;
His long-tailed mouse that pranced so gay
Had stolen away.

So he had to harness an honest toad
To his mushroom car, and take the road.
Twice on the way his car broke down;
And while he patched it with sticks and things,
He was heard to say, "By black and by brown,"
He was tempted to take to his wings.
But safely he reached the fairies' hall
And was kindly and gayly greeted by all.

Now Bibbetybobble and Kickittygo and Floppyfly
Were terribly sly;
When they found themselves on the mountain alone,
They guessed where Rufflecumtuffle had gone,
        And wanted to go themselves—
        The silly, comical elves!

So they harnessed a turtle safe and slow
To their family coach, and Kickittygo
Held the reins and flourished the whip;
And down with a bump and a slip
They rode until they reached the fairies' hall,
And were kindly greeted and welcomed by all.

Rufflecumtuffle was striding about
With his head thrown back, and his chest thrown out,
And he held himself so stiff and prim
That the fairies would surely have laughed at him
    If they had not been quite
    Too good and polite.
He had danced and danced with the prettiest fay,
And twisted his mustache every way,
    And paraded his wings
    With the gold and scarlet rings
    And felt so vain and proud
    That he almost chuckled aloud.

But when he saw his brothers three
Come rubbing their hands in elvish glee,
    With shame and dismay
    He almost fainted away.
    But a fairy flew
For a cup of the strongest perfumed dew,

And gave him to drink; and they brought sweet wine
Out of the red-horned columbine;
And passed it around to the elves,
        Who then straightway
        Became so gay
That they hardly knew how to contain themselves;
And when the ravishing music began,
The fairy flutes and viols sweet,
Then it was that each elvish man
Felt such a lightness in his feet,
That snatching the hand of the nearest fay,
Round they whisked in the wildest way
Oh! I wish, I *wish* you had been that way
To see them curvet and see them prance!
Bibbetybobble tumbled about
Just like a fat old bumble bee;
Floppyfly you could hardly see,
He went so fast; and Kickittygo—
His legs like the spokes of a wheel rayed out;
And Rufflecumtuffle—you never will know
How he danced, for I never can tell;
And Oh! 'twas a wonderful sight for me
        And if ever again
        The elvish men
With the fairies dance, you must go and see.

And here is the Music for

Little Dame Crump
Merry Green Fields of England
The Old Gray Goose
Joe Dobson
Old Mother Tabbyskins
The Hungry Fox
Frog Went A-Courting
The Keys of Heaven
The Old Crow
Old Crummles
We Are All Nodding
Mr. Bourne and His Wife
Cluck, Cluck

LITTLE DAME CRUMP

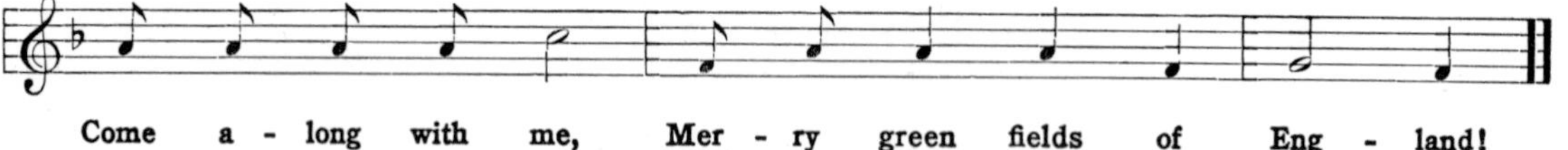

THE OLD GRAY GOOSE

JOE DOBSON

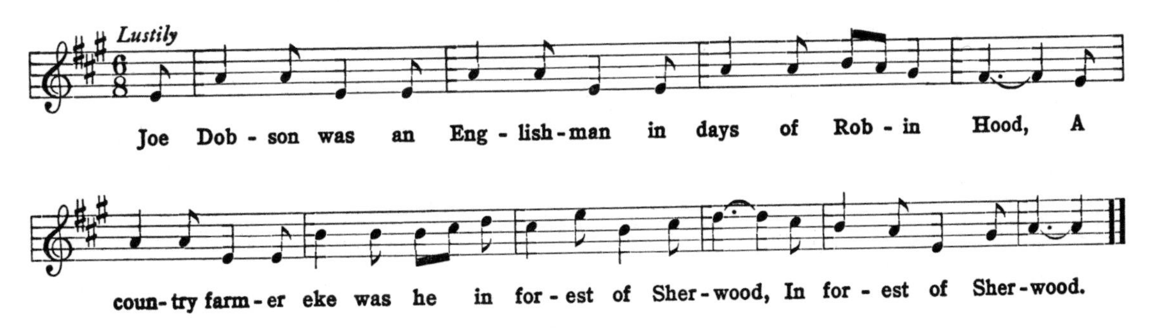

OLD MOTHER TABBYSKINS

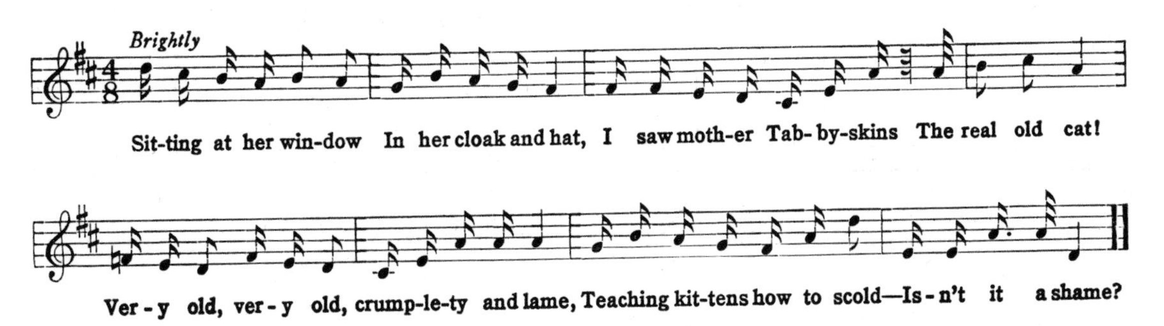

THE HUNGRY FOX
With emphasis
A fox went out in a hun - gry plight, And he begged of the moon to
give him some light, For he had man - y miles to trav - el that night, Be -
fore he reached his den - o, den - o, den - o, For he
had man - y miles to trav - el that night, Be - fore he reached his den - o!
FROG WENT A-COURTING
Not too fast
Frog went a - court - ing he did ride a - hum, a - hum. Frog went a - court - ing
he did ride, sword and pis - tol by his side A - hum, A - hum!
THE KEYS OF HEAVEN
Lightly
I'll give to you a pa - per of pins, For that's the way true love be - gins, If
you will mar - ry me, me, me, If you will mar - ry me!

THE OLD CROW

OLD CRUMMLES

This keeps repeating over and over until end of song.

WE ARE ALL NODDING